Garfield
Le Magnifique!

JiM DAViS

ℛℛ
RAVETTE BOOKS

First published by Ravette Books Limited 1990
Reprinted 1990, 1991 (twice), 1993

Printed and bound in Great Britain
for Ravette Books Limited,
8 Clifford Street,
London W1X 1RB
An Egmont Company
by Cox & Wyman Ltd, Reading

ISBN 1 85304 243 9

1-31

HI, ODIE!

© 1989 United Feature Syndicate, Inc.

THAT WAS TOO EASY

THUD!

JIM DAVIS

© 1989 United Feature Syndicate, Inc.

2-2

BWOING!

© 1989 United Feature Syndicate, Inc.

BREAKFAST IN BED, GARFIELD?

SLOTH IS THE MOTHER OF INVENTION

JPM DAVPS

DOGS ARE THE ANIMAL BY-PRODUCTS IN THE WEENIE OF LIFE

DEPRESSED, GARFIELD?

© 1989 United Feature Syndicate, Inc.

HOW COULD YOU TELL?

JIM DAVIS

JIM DAVIS

2-10

© 1989 United Feature Syndicate, Inc.

WHIRR

2-14

JiM DAViS

JIM DAVIS 2-15

© 1989 United Feature Syndicate, Inc.

© 1989 United Feature Syndicate, Inc.

© 1989 United Feature Syndicate, Inc.

WHAT DO YOU GET WHEN YOU CROSS
A DOG WITH A NINE-FOOT GORILLA?

3-1   JIM DAVIS

YOU GET A GORILLA THAT DRINKS
OUT OF ANY TOILET HE PLEASES!

3-7

© 1989 United Feature Syndicate, Inc.

POIT

JiM DAViS 3-13

SNIP!

AIEEEEE

3-14

WHAP!

JIM DAVIS

JIM DAVIS

3-16

SQUISH

JIM DAVIS

3-17

"WHAP!"

© 1989 United Feature Syndicate, Inc.

JIM DAVIS 3-18

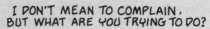

© 1989 United Feature Syndicate, Inc.

SHTOING!

© 1989 United Feature Syndicate, Inc

THANK GOODNESS
I MISSED THE
APPLE

JIM DAVIS

3-28

3-31 JIM DAVIS

© 1989 United Feature Syndicate, Inc.

JIM DAVIS   4-3

P.SHHHHH

4-5 JIM DAVIS

© 1989 United Feature Syndicate, Inc.

SCRIBBLE
SCRIBBLE
SCRIBBLE

CATS
STINK

JIM DAVIS

4·8

4-10

© 1989 United Feature Syndicate, Inc.

JIM DAVIS

4-14

GOOD, GARFIELD'S NOT AROUND.
I WON'T HAVE TO SHARE MY MILK

JIM DAVIS   4-20

© 1989 United Feature Syndicate, Inc.

JIM DAVIS 5-6

5-16

JPM DAVPS

5-27

JIM DAVIS

5-29

5-30

© 1989 United Feature Syndicate, Inc.

6-16

OTHER GARFIELD BOOKS IN THIS SERIES

COLOUR TV SPECIALS

Here Comes Garfield	£2.95
Garfield On The Town	£2.95
Garfield In The Rough	£2.95
Garfield In Disguise	£2.95
Garfield In Paradise	£2.95
Garfield Goes To Hollywood	£2.95
A Garfield Christmas	£2.95
Garfield's Thanksgiving	£2.95
Garfield's Feline Fantasies	£2.95
Garfield Gets A Life	£2.95
Garfield's Night Before Christmas	£3.95
Garfield's Tales Of Mystery	£3.95
Garfield's Scary Tales	£3.95
Garfield The Easter Bunny?	£3.95
Garfield Best Ever	£4.95
Garfield Selection	£5.95
Garfield His 9 Lives	£5.95
Garfield Diet Book	£4.95
Garfield Exercise Book	£4.95
Garfield Book Of Love	£2.99

All these books are available at your local bookshop or newsagent, or can be ordered direct from the publisher. Just tick the titles you require and fill in the form below. Prices and availability subject to change without notice.

Ravette Books, PO Box 11, Falmouth, Cornwall, TR10 9EN.

Please send a cheque or postal order for the value of the book, and add the following for postage and packing:
UK including BFPO – £1.00 per order.
OVERSEAS, including EIRE – £2.00 per order.
OR Please debit this amount from my Access/Visa Card (delete as appropriate).

Card Number

AMOUNT £ .... EXPIRY DATE ....

SIGNED ....

NAME ....

ADDRESS ....

....